Jess, Tom and Adam were friends.

Mrs Patel was their teacher.

It was time for lunch and all the

children got their lunch boxes.

Mrs Patel opened her lunch box.

'Oh no!' she said.

All the children looked at Mrs Patel.

'My lunch is not here!'
said Mrs Patel.

Jess went up to Mrs Patel.

'You can eat my banana,'
said Jess.

Tom went up to Mrs Patel.

'You can eat my crisps,'
said Tom.

Adam went up to Mrs Patel.

'You can eat my sandwich,'
said Adam.

'Here is my cake,' said Jess.

'Here is my apple,' said Tom.

'Now you can eat,' said Jess.
'Yes I can,' said Mrs Patel.
'Yum, yum!'